CARL FISCHER MUSIC LIBRARY—L110

# Studies for Violin

## Part 1 - Twenty Studies in the First Position

## Op. 32

SAENGER

# Preface.

Considering the best foundation of violin technique to be a thorough command of the first 5 positions, I have written the following little Études, through which an opportunity is afforded the beginner of familiarizing himself with these essential elements of violin-playing to a degree, not offered by the exercises of Violin-schools in general.

The character of these Études is such, that they can be progressively used in connection with any Violin-school, and offer the pupil both the study of the positions and considerable variety in Time and Bowing.

# Vorwort.

*Für die beste Grundlage des Violinspiels die vollständige Beherrschung der ersten 5 Lagen haltend, habe ich nachstehende kleine Etuden geschrieben, welche dem Anfänger Gelegenheit geben sollen, sich mit diesen Grundelementen des Violinspiels noch vertrauter zu machen als es das Übungsmaterial mancher Violinschule bietet.*

*Die Beschaffenheit dieser Etuden ist derartig, dass dieselben beim Unterricht neben jeder Violinschule fortschreitend benützt werden können und dem Schüler neben den Lagenstudien mancherlei Abwechslung in Takt und Stricharten bringen.*

# 20 STUDIES
## in the first Position.

Revised and fingered by Gustav Saenger.

HANS SITT, Op.32. Part I.

⊓ Down-Bow.
V Up-Bow.

Divide your bow
Whole bows
Moderato.
2.
play it
Moderato.
3.

Moderato.
4.

5.
Moderato.
6.

**Andante.**

7.

Moderato.
8.
Moderato.
9.

Allegro.
10.

Moderato.
11.

Allegro moderato.

Moderato.
13.

**Allegro moderato.**

14.

Moderato.
15.

Allegro.

Allegro.
17.

**Moderato.**

Moderato assai.
19.

Moderato.



20.

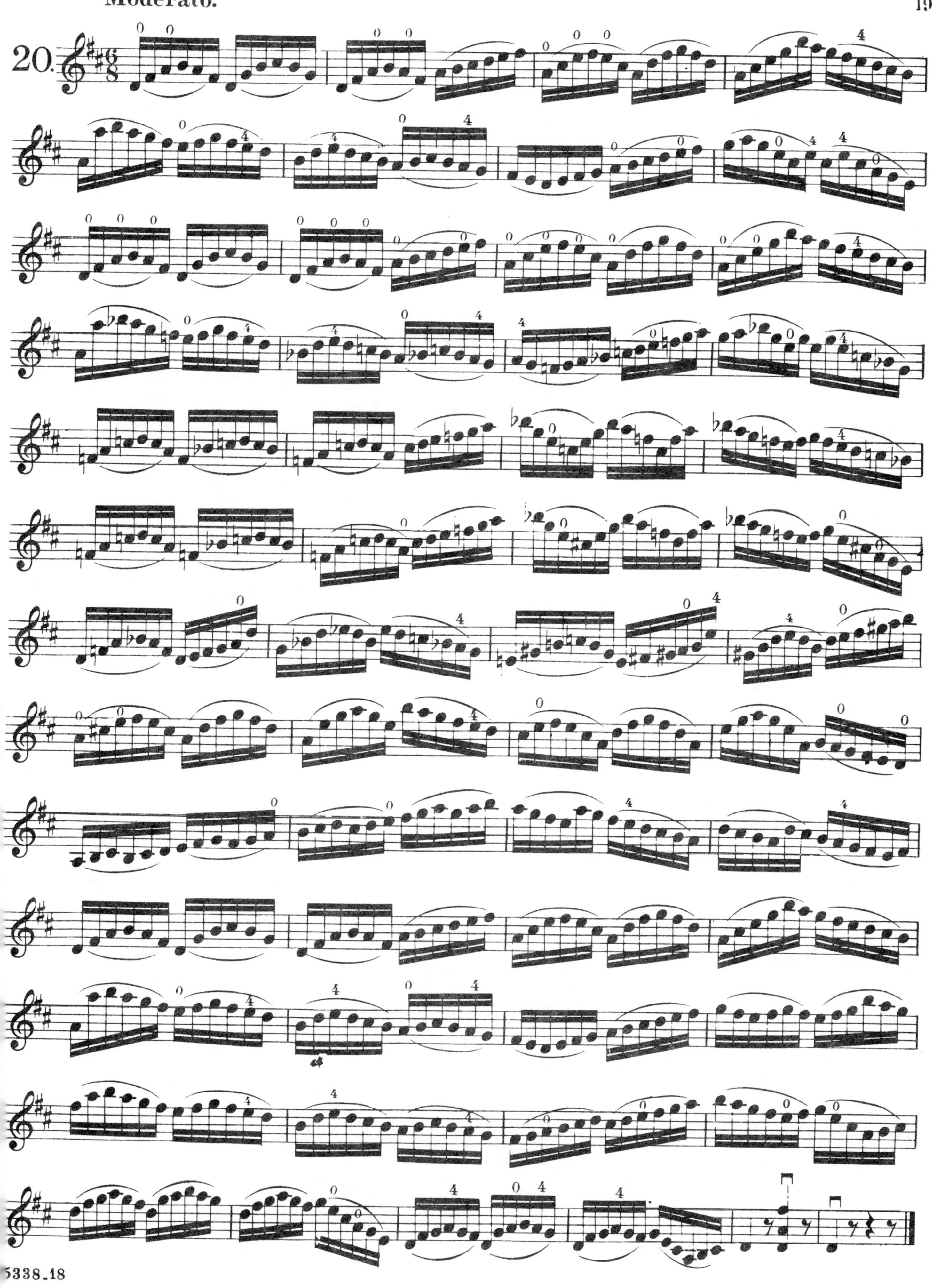

# Jascha Heifetz Folios

**"The Heifetz Collection" for Violin & Piano**
A collection of twenty-four classic Heifetz transcriptions along with a bonus of two violin concerto cadenzas that are part of the legacy and legend of the "father of modern, virtuoso violin playing." This edition contains separate piano and violin parts, that are expertly edited, engraved and printed to provide many years of use and pleasure. Foreword by Itzhak Perlman.
(Cat. No. ATF116)

---

**"New Favorite Encore Folio" for Violin & Piano**
This fine collection of fifteen compositions was selected and edited by Heifetz and presented in outstanding engravings and printing. Compositions include "Rigaudon", "Zapateado," "Guitarre" in addition to pieces by Schubert, Mendelssohn, Mozart, Brahms and Schumann among others.
(Cat. No. O2137)

Jascha Heifetz
JH
New
Favorite Encore Folio
for Violin and Piano
CARL FISCHER